SINGAPOREAN NURSERY

JACK AND JILL
AT BUKIT TIMAH HILL

Gwen Lee

Illustrated by twisstii

E

EPIGRAM BOOKS / SINGAPORE

Peter, Peter, Durian Eater

Peter, Peter, durian eater,
Ate so many he shocked his mother;
She gave him salt water in the shell,
To drink and gargle away the smell.

Peter, Peter, durian eater,
Ate so many he began to teeter;
Got sent to bed with so much brine,
He dreamt he ate a porcupine.

Curry at the Night Safari

I went to the Night Safari,
The lion was cooking curry,
The pangolins by the light of the moon
Came to join the party.
The leopard, annoyed by the smell,
Said he felt quite unwell,
But when he slurped up some spicy gravy,
He thought it was really swell!

Little Boy Boo

Little Boy Boo,
Come down to play,
The void deck's all empty,
We'll have a field day;
Where are the boys
Who scored between the pillars?
They're in the classrooms
Trying to be winners.
Will you be the goalie?
Oh no, not I,
For if I do
Mom's sure to cry.

Ride a Bumboat to Chek Jawa

Ride a slow bumboat to Chek Jawa,
To see a biologist dance the samba;
With birds on her shoulders and crabs on her toes,
She shall have nature wherever she goes.

This Old Man

This old man, he played one,
He played Zeropoint under the sun;
Having fun with a friend,
Without getting out of hand,
This is a game I'd recommend.

This old man, he played two,
He played Capteh on my shoe;
Having fun with a friend,
Without getting out of hand,
This is a game I'd recommend.

This old man, he played three,
He played goli on his knee;
Having fun with a friend,
Without getting out of hand,
This is a game I'd recommend.

This old man, he played four,
He played Hopscotch on the floor;
Having fun with a friend,
Without getting out of hand,
This is a game I'd recommend.

This old man, he played five,
He played Five Stones with Sir Clive;
Having fun with a friend,
Without getting out of hand,
This is a game I'd recommend.

Spice Girl, Spice Girl, Nature Lover

Spice Girl, Spice Girl, nature lover.
How does your garden grow?
With cardamom and cinnamon,
And cumin plants all in a row.

Cardamom

A Tisket, A Tasket

A tisket, a tasket,
A bamboo dim sum basket,
I piled it high with hot siew mai,
And in my haste I dropped it.
I dropped it, I dropped it,
And in my haste I dropped it.
A little boy picked it up
And wrapped it in his jacket.

He was hanging around the restaurant,
Who knows where his mom had gone?
He was pushing the trolley all around,
When he spied it on the ground.
He took it, he took it,
My bamboo dim sum basket.
Oh little boy, do bring it back,
'Cause I don't want to lose my snack.

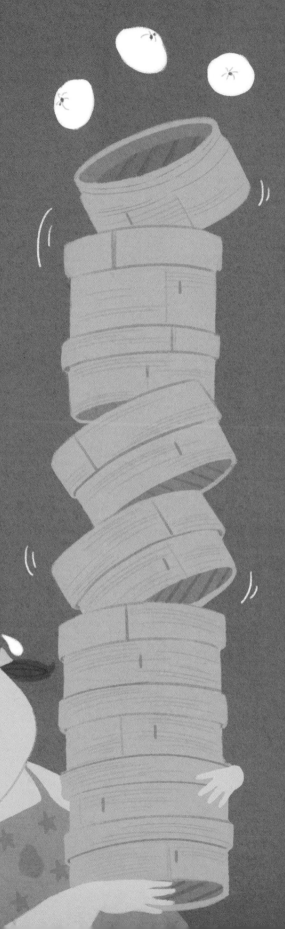

A tisket, a tasket,
A bamboo dim sum basket,
I piled it high with lo mai gai,
And in my haste I dropped it.
I dropped it, I dropped it,
And in my haste I dropped it.
A little boy picked it up
And hid it in his blanket.

He was stacking the baskets way up high,
Very soon they'll touch the sky.
He placed my basket right on top,
Please, can someone make him stop?
He took it, he took it,
My bamboo dim sum basket.
Oh little boy, do bring it back,
'Cause I don't want a heart attack.

I Had a Little Rain Tree

I had a little Rain Tree,
Nothing would it bear,
But colourful and
Polka-dotted underwear.

The Marshal of Mandai
Came to visit me.
"It's better than my bonsai!"
He praised my little tree.

But all the jealous kids,
They plucked the underwear,
Used them as hats and bibs,
Pulled right over their hair.

Since that day so long ago,
Never did I see,
Pretty underwear grow
From my little Rain Tree.

I poured lots of water,
I almost poured the sea,
But only pink flowers
Grew from my little tree.

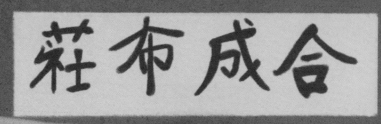

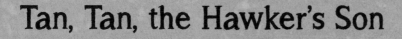

Tan, Tan, the Hawker's Son

Tan, Tan, the hawker's son,
Stole ice kachang, and away did run;
Soon the ice melted,
Tan's caper ended,
Tan went crying
Down the street.

Badang Was a Strong Man

Badang was a poor man, the genie was a thief;
The genie ate up Badang's fish and left him in disbelief;
Badang caught the genie and demanded back his fish;
Until it begged for mercy and promised to grant a wish.

Badang was a small man who wanted to be tough;
He drank the genie's vomit and became strong and buff;
India sent Bijaya to put Badang to the test;
Whoever could throw the huge rock would be proclaimed the best.

Badang was a strong man, Bijaya was not weak;
But when Bijaya tried to move the rock, you could hear him weep.
Badang lifted it above his head and without the slightest moan,
Threw it into the sea, where it became the Singapore Stone.

Mary Had an Orang Utan

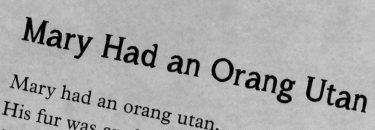

Mary had an orang utan,
His fur was apple red,
And everywhere that Mary went,
The ape would run ahead.

He followed her to the library,
Where he hoped he could relax,
He sneaked in oh-so-quietly
And camped among the stacks.

When the ape began to read,
He learnt his home was the jungle.
All at once he asked to be freed,
And for Mary to end this bungle.

"Set me free if you love me so,"
The ape said with a cry.
"But your forest is gone, you know."
Poor Mary did reply.

Kueh Tutu

Kueh tutu!
Kueh tutu!
One a dollar, two a dollar,
Kueh tutu!
Coconut or peanut,
Either one will do.
One a dollar,
Two a dollar,
Kueh tutu!

It's Raining; It's Pouring

It's raining, it's pouring.
The monsoon is coming.
Southwest, northeast, winds are blowing.
June to September, and in December.

Jack and Jill at Bukit Timah Hill

Jack and Jill went up the hill,
To find the Monkey Man;
Jack fell down, and claimed he was ill,
Leaving Jill without a plan.
Jill trekked through Bukit Timah,
With all the strength she could muster;
She climbed so high and up so far,
The birds all twittered in wonder.

On top of the peak,
She was too scared to speak,
When she came upon a tiger;
But he offered her fruit,
And told her, "Don't shoot!
For that would be a real disaster."

The Original Rhymes

Peter, Peter, Pumpkin Eater
(America, 19TH Century)
Peter, Peter, pumpkin eater,
Had a wife and couldn't keep her;
He put her in a pumpkin shell,
And there he kept her very well.

The Animal Fair
(America, 19TH Century)
I went to the animal fair,
The birds and the beasts were there,
The old baboon by the light
of the moon
Was combing his auburn hair.
The monkey he got drunk,
And fell on the elephant's trunk;
The elephant sneezed and went down
on his knees,
And what became of the monk?

Little Boy Blue
(England, 18TH Century)
Little Boy Blue,
Come blow your horn,
The sheep's in the meadow,
The cow's in the corn;
Where is that boy
Who looks after the sheep?
He's under the haystack
Fast asleep.
Will you wake him?
Oh no, not I,
For if I do
He's sure to cry.

Ride a Cock Horse to Banbury Cross
(England, 18TH Century)
Ride a cock horse to Banbury Cross,
To see a fine lady upon a white horse;
With rings on her fingers and bells
on her toes,
She shall have music wherever she goes.

This Old Man
(England, 20TH Century)
This old man, he played one,
He played knick-knack on my thumb;
With a knick-knack paddywhack,
Give the dog a bone,
This old man came rolling home.

This old man, he played two,
He played knick-knack on my shoe;
With a knick-knack paddywhack,
Give the dog a bone,
This old man came rolling home.

This old man, he played three,
He played knick-knack on my knee;
With a knick-knack paddywhack,
Give the dog a bone,
This old man came rolling home.

This old man, he played four,
He played knick-knack on my door;
With a knick-knack paddywhack,
Give the dog a bone,
This old man came rolling home.

This old man, he played five,
He played knick-knack on my hive;
With a knick-knack paddywhack,
Give the dog a bone,
This old man came rolling home.

Mary, Mary, Quite Contrary
(England, 18TH Century)
Mary, Mary, quite contrary
How does your garden grow?
With silver bells and cockleshells
And pretty maids all in a row.

A Tisket, A Tasket
(America, 19TH Century)
A tisket, a tasket,
A green and yellow basket,
I wrote a letter to my love,
And on the way I dropped it.
I dropped it, I dropped it,
And on the way I dropped it.
A little boy picked it up
And put it in his pocket.

I Had a Little Nut Tree
(England, 18TH Century)
I had a little nut tree,
Nothing would it bear,
But a silver nutmeg
And a golden pear.
The King of Spain's daughter
Came to visit me,
And all for the sake
Of my little nut tree.

Her dress was made of crimson,
Jet black was her hair,
She asked me for my nutmeg
And my golden pear.

I said, "So fair a princess
Never did I see,
I'll give you all the fruit
From my little nut tree."

I danced o'er the water,
I danced o'er the sea,
And all the birds in the air,
Couldn't catch me.

Tom, Tom, the Piper's Son
(England, 18TH Century)
Tom, Tom, the piper's son,
Stole a pig, and away did run;
The pig was eat
And Tom was beat,
And Tom went crying
Down the street.

Taffy Was a Welshman
(England, 18TH Century)

Taffy was a Welshman,
Taffy was a thief;
Taffy came to my house
and stole a piece of beef;
I went to Taffy's house, Taffy wasn't in;
I jumped upon his Sunday hat and
poked it with a pin.
Taffy was a Welshman, Taffy was a sham;
Taffy came to my house and stole
a piece of lamb;
I went to Taffy's house, Taffy was away,
I stuffed his socks with sawdust and
filled his shoes with clay.
Taffy was a Welshman, Taffy was a cheat;
Taffy came to my house,
and stole a piece of meat;
I went to Taffy's house,
Taffy was not there,
I hung his coat and trousers
to roast before a fire.

Mary Had a Little Lamb
(America, 19TH Century)

Mary had a little lamb,
His fleece was white as snow,
And everywhere that Mary went,
The lamb was sure to go.

He followed her to school one day,
Which was against the rule,
It made the children laugh and play
To see a lamb at school.

And so the teacher turned it out,
But still it lingered near,
And waited patiently about,
Till Mary did appear.

"Why does the lamb love Mary so?"
The eager children cry.
"Why, Mary loves the lamb, you know."
The teacher did reply.

Hot Cross Buns
(England, 18TH Century)

Hot cross buns!
Hot cross buns!
One a penny, two a penny,
Hot cross buns!
If you have no daughters,
Give them to your sons.
One a penny,
Two a penny,
Hot cross buns!

It's Raining; It's Pouring
(America, 20TH Century)

It's raining; it's pouring.
The old man is snoring.
He went to bed and bumped his head,
And he wouldn't get up in the morning.

Jack and Jill
(England, 18TH Century)

Jack and Jill went up the hill,
To fetch a pail of water;
Jack fell down, and broke his crown,
And Jill came tumbling after.
Then up Jack got and off did trot,
As fast as he could caper,
To old Dame Dob, who patched his nob
With vinegar and brown paper.
When Jill came in,
How she did grin
To see Jack's paper plaster;
Her mother, vexed,
Did whip her next,
For laughing at Jack's disaster.

Brainy Bites

Peter, Peter, Durian Eater
Grown in Southeast Asia, the durian tree produces fruit twice a year. The Chinese believe that the durian is a "heaty" fruit. In the past, people would drink water—sometimes mixed with salt—from empty durian husks as a post-durian drink to "cool" down their bodies.

Curry at the Night Safari
Opened in 1994, Singapore's Night Safari is the world's first safari park for nocturnal animals. It is also the first in the world to have successfully bred the Sunda pangolin—a scaly animal whose tongue is longer than its body.

Little Boy Boo
The large concrete spaces at the bottom of Housing and Development Board (HDB) blocks are called "void decks". These sheltered spaces were often used as football grounds by children until HDB put up signs banning the practice.

Ride a Bumboat to Chek Jawa
Chek Jawa is an intertidal flat on Pulau Ubin, an island near Singapore. Many creatures such as mudskippers, starfishes and crabs make their home on Chek Jawa's shores and mangrove forests. At certain times of the year, you can even find colourful sea cucumbers in its seagrass lagoon.

This Old Man
Zeropoint, Capteh, Goli, Hopscotch and Five Stones are all traditional games played by Singaporean children. They are not only fun, but improve your dexterity.

Sir Clive Wentworth Uhr (1903–1974) was an Australian radiologist who was imprisoned in Changi by the Japanese during World War II. During his captivity, he continued to provide medical care for his fellow prisoners. He was knighted in 1972.

Spice Girl, Spice Girl, Nature Lover
A spice is a dried fruit, seed, bark or root of a plant used to flavour, colour or preserve food. Did you know that dried cinnamon is obtained from the bark of the Cinnamon Tree?

A Tisket, A Tasket
Dim sum, a Cantonese style of food, is traditionally served in small steamer baskets made of bamboo. Servers in a restaurant would push around stacks of these baskets on trolleys for customers to choose their orders while seated at their tables.

I Had a Little Rain Tree
The local Rain Tree has a big umbrella-shaped crown. It is called the Rain Tree because its leaves fold up before rainy weather.

Tan, Tan, the Hawker's Son
The ice kachang is the modern version of the ice ball sold by pushcart vendors in the 1950s and 1960s. "Kachang" means "beans" in the Malay language.

Badang Was a Strong Man
The rock in the legend of Badang is believed to be the stone found at the mouth of the Singapore River in 1819. However, before the ancient inscriptions on the stone could be deciphered, the British Settlement Engineer, Captain Stevenson, had it blown up to pieces in 1843. A fragment of the Singapore Stone can be seen at the National Museum of Singapore.

Mary Had an Orang Utan
The name "orang utan" means "person of the forest". Found only in the rainforests of Sumatra and Borneo, these great apes are among the most intelligent primates. Sadly, orang utans face a high risk of extinction because of human activities like logging and hunting.

Kueh Tutu
Kueh tutu is a flower-shaped steamed cake made of rice flour and filled with either ground peanuts or grated coconut. Served on a piece of pandan leaf, kueh tutu is unique to Singapore.

It's Raining; It's Pouring
A monsoon is a seasonal wind that lasts for several months. It brings moderate to heavy rains and lower temperatures. There are two monsoon seasons in Singapore. The Southwest Monsoon season occurs from June to September, while the Northeast Monsoon happens from December to early March.

Jack and Jill at Bukit Timah Hill
Bukit Timah Hill, Singapore's tallest hill, stands at 162.5 metres above sea level and is home to the myth of the Monkey Man. Reportedly spotted by locals since 1805, the Monkey Man is a creature who walks like a man but has the face of a monkey. Another creature that made Bukit Timah its home was the Malayan Tiger. The last tiger at Bukit Timah Hill was shot in 1924. No others have been spotted since the 1940s.